GREAT TED TALKS
JOURNAL

Portable Press
An imprint of Printers Row Publishing Group
10350 Barnes Canyon Road, Suite 100, San Diego, CA 92121
www.portablepress.com • mail@portablepress.com

Printers Row Publishing Group is a division of Readerlink Distribution Services, LLC. Portable Press is a registered trademark of Readerlink Distribution Services, LLC.

Correspondence regarding the content of this book should be sent to Portable Press, Editorial Department, at the above address. Author and illustration inquiries should be sent to Quarto Publishing Plc, 6 Blundell St, London N7 9BH, www.quartoknows.com.

Portable Press
Publisher: Peter Norton • Associate Publisher: Ana Parker
Senior Developmental Editor: April Graham Farr
Senior Product Manager: Kathryn C. Dalby

Produced by Quarto Publishing plc
Publisher: Mark Searle
Creative Director: James Evans
Art Director: Katherine Radcliffe
Commissioning Editor: Sorrel Wood
Managing Editors: Isheeta Mustafi and Jacqui Sayers
In-house Editor: Abbie Sharman
Editor: David Price-Goodfellow • Designer: Tony Seddon

ISBN: 978-1-64517-381-6

Printed in China

24 23 22 21 20   1 2 3 4 5

GREAT
TED
TALKS
JOURNAL

An Unofficial Guided Journal with 36 Interactive Exercises

**PORTABLE
PRESS**

San Diego, California

CONTENTS

INTRODUCTION 6

HOW TO USE THIS BOOK 8

EXERCISES FOR CREATIVITY 10

TAKE THE THIRTY-DAY CHALLENGE 12
LISTEN TO YOUNGER PEOPLE 16
PLAY A WORD GAME 20
DOODLE IN MEETINGS 26
TURN OUT THE LIGHTS 30
DESIRE PATHS 34
YOUR IMPERFECT RÉSUMÉ 40
REJECTION BUCKET LIST 46
POSITIVE EXPERIENCE 52
WHAT IS FAILURE? 56
THE "CAN'T-DO" LIST 60
ANCESTRAL BACKGROUND MAP 66
MY MULTIPOTENTIALITY 70
DRAW YOUR PERSONAL FUTURE 76

EXERCISES FOR INNOVATION 78

KNOW YOUR BLIND SPOTS 80
CHALLENGE YOURSELF 84
DISRUPT OR BE DISRUPTED 88
ASK FOR HELP 94
A NEW CORPORATE DEMOCRACY 98
THE NEW RULES OF INNOVATION 104
EXPLORE THE WEIRD AND UNKNOWN 108
FAILING MINDFULLY 112
SPACE TO CREATE 116
CHANGING THE WORLD 120
TAKE CONTROL OF YOUR DESTINY 124

EXERCISES FOR LEADERSHIP   126

STRESS IS YOUR FRIEND   128
KEEP IT SIMPLE   134
FIND A MENTOR   142
DON'T FORGET TO FORGET   148
STAND OUT   154
YOU'RE ALREADY A LEADER   160
GET PRAISE   166
MINDFUL CURIOSITY   172
RESPECT IS KEY   178
KNOW YOUR IMPACT   182
YOU CAN'T KNOW EVERYTHING   188

INTRODUCTION

Do you want to shift your thinking, open your mind to new perspectives, or simply achieve your full potential at work, home, or in life? Welcome to the world of TED via this unofficial guided journal with interactive excercises—the perfect thought-provoking, brain-boosting, doodle-encouraging companion to **Great TED Talks: Creativity**, **Great TED Talks: Innovation**, and **Great TED Talks: Leadership**.

Riffing on over 300 of the most powerful TED talks relating to creativity, innovation, and leadership—across fields as diverse as technology, entertainment, and design (the original TED trio)—this handy guide is packed with motivating quotes and exercises to get your juices flowing, help you think outside of the box, cement your values, and inspire meaningful action or change.

Learn how to be strategic and visionary from masters such as Bill Gates, Gary Vaynerchuk, and Judson Brewer. Be open to new ways of thinking that could help unlock a creative block a la Sunni Brown and Julie Burstein. Find eureka moments in unusual places or encounter new mindful ways to work from the likes of Heidi Grant or Elizabeth Gilbert.

There's also plenty of space to write down your own thoughts, inspired by the insightful views of **Great TED Talk** authors Tom May, Neil C. Hughes, and Harriet Minter, so keep your journal handy to your most contemplative spaces—your desk space, work bag, or even by your bed. A few mindful minutes is all you need to reboot your brain.

Initially conceived by Richard Saul Wurman in 1984 as an annual conference where Technology, Entertainment, and Design converged, thousands of TED talks delivered by a global array of the most inspired thinkers, leaders, and teachers in topics as diverse as science, music, philosophy, and design are now available online. The mission—to spread ideas to people from every discipline and culture via short, powerful talks of 18 minutes or less, with the power to change ideas, lives, and ultimately, the world. Find out more at ted.com.

REMOVING FEAR FROM THE INNOVATION EQUATION CAN MAKE THE IMPOSSIBLE POSSIBLE.

NEIL C. HUGHES, *GREAT TED TALKS: INNOVATION*, PAGE 124

HOW TO USE THIS BOOK

Feeling switched on by the world of TED? Itching to put some ideas into action or make an inspired plan? Turn the page or open at random to begin your journey through a journal of brain boosting, mind-expanding quotes and exercises designed to help you do just that.

You'll need a pen or pencil at the ready and possibly a pack of sticky notes or extra paper in case you need more room to explore your thoughts. A quiet space and hot drink can also help to create the right environment and mood—although, be warned: many of the quotes and exercises within this book could turn an everyday tea or coffee break into a game-changing one.

There are then multiple ways to use this book. Work from front to back, like a diary, using the added content as a trigger for or accompaniment to your own to-do lists, actions, and ideas. Treat it as an activity book and see where each suggestion takes you; take your cue from "Try Something New for Thirty Days" (see page 12) and allocate a particular time each day for a month when it's just you and your journal. Or dip in and out when the moment arises, on the bus or just before bed perhaps, getting involved when a quote or exercise particularly inspires—a meditative doodling session or a wordplay game perhaps.

Revisiting relevant commentaries in *Great TED Talks: Creativity*, *Innovation*, or *Leadership* might also be the perfect way to trigger a long sought-after "Aha!" moment, so look out for the talk information underneath the quotes. As Tom May says, "stop being so 'adult' and let your imagination fly" (*Great TED Talks: Creativity*, page 10).

Find out more

These boxes give you the page information so you can read the full commentary about the exercises and provides the TED talk information.

EXPAND THE WAY YOU THINK ABOUT THE FUTURE, AND IT COULD ALSO HELP YOU CREATE BETTER WORK IN THE PRESENT.

TOM MAY, *GREAT TED TALKS: CREATIVITY,* **PAGE 176**

EXERCISES

FOR

CREATIVITY

1. TAKE THE THIRTY-DAY CHALLENGE

Do you have something you'd love to try or a habit you'd like to change? Giving yourself a thirty-day challenge could be the answer.

Set yourself a simple challenge, for example reading a book every night for a month, and check the days off the calendar opposite as you complete them. You should find that after thirty days you are enjoying this new activity as part of your routine.

IT TURNS OUT THIRTY DAYS IS JUST ABOUT THE RIGHT AMOUNT OF TIME TO ADD A NEW HABIT OR SUBTRACT A HABIT—LIKE WATCHING THE NEWS—FROM YOUR LIFE . . . SO WHY NOT THINK ABOUT SOMETHING YOU'VE ALWAYS WANTED TO TRY AND GIVE IT A SHOT, FOR THE NEXT THIRTY DAYS.

From "Try Something New for Thirty Days" (2011)

🔍 For more ideas about learning a new skill, see page 12 of *Great TED Talks: Creativity*

01.	02.	03.	04.	05.
06.	07.	08.	09.	10.
11.	12.	13.	14.	15.
16.	17.	18.	19.	20.
21.	22.	23.	24.	25.
26.	27.	28.	29.	30.

STOP BEING SO "ADULT" AND LET YOUR IMAGINATION FLY.

Tom May,
Great TED Talks: Creativity, page 10.

2. LISTEN TO YOUNGER PEOPLE

Have you got creative block? Are you thinking of asking for advice? Taking a moment to think about the people you might approach for help could be the key to unlocking your potential.

Use the exercise opposite to list the people you can inspire and the people that you can learn from. We often look to our elders when we are in need of advice but taking the time to identify people of all ages that can inspire you will result in a better range of ideas. Remember, knowledge can flow both ways.

THE MODERN ELDER IS AS MUCH AN INTERN AS . . . A MENTOR. THEY REALIZE, IN A WORLD THAT IS CHANGING SO QUICKLY [A MILLENNIAL'S] BEGINNER'S MIND AND THEIR CATALYTIC CURIOSITY IS A LIFE-AFFIRMING ELIXIR, NOT JUST FOR THEMSELVES BUT FOR EVERYONE AROUND THEM.

From "What Baby Boomers Can Learn from Millennials at Work—and Vice Versa" (2018)

For insights into sharing knowledge across the age divide, see page 20 of *Great TED Talks: Creativity*

People I inspire:　　　　　　　　**People I learn from:**

ENCOUNTERING DIFFERENT PERSPECTIVES IS A GREAT WAY TO STIMULATE NEW CREATIVE IDEAS. AND ONE OF THE EASIEST WAYS TO DO THIS IS TO TAP INTO PEOPLE FROM DIFFERENT GENERATIONS.

Tom May,
*Great TED Talks:
Creativity*, page 20.

3. PLAY A WORD GAME

Are you struggling to get ideas to come to you? This simple word game will help.

On the page opposite, write the first word that comes to your mind. Now come up with another word that starts with the letter that the first word ends with (such as apple, elephant, trumpet). Once you've got the hang of this try thinking about the words and ideas on a secondary level. For example, if you're trying to invent a new toy, try connecting the words you're producing with a toy. If you think of enough ideas eventually you'll have a good one—at least that's the idea.

THE MORE IDEAS YOU PRODUCE, [THE MORE] YOU'RE SURE TO COME UP WITH SOME GOOD ONES, TOO.

From "Play This Word Game to
Come Up with Original Ideas" (2013)

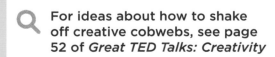

For ideas about how to shake off creative cobwebs, see page 52 of *Great TED Talks: Creativity*

WHEN WE SET OUT TO BE CREATIVE, WE OBVIOUSLY WANT OUR WORK TO BE ORIGINAL. BUT THAT DOESN'T MEAN WE CAN'T BE INSPIRED BY OTHERS.

Tom May,
Great TED Talks: Creativity, page 22.

OVERCOME YOUR FEARS, STEP BY STEP.

Tom May,
Great TED Talks: Creativity, page 23.

4. DOODLE IN MEETINGS

Doodling during meetings rather than taking notes doesn't need to be a negative. Turn it into a positive by using it to stir your creative juices and come up with some new ideas.

This tried-and-tested method is a great way for your mind to process information in a creative way. It engages the four ways to take in infomation (reading and writing, visual, auditory, and tactile) and allows you to engage on an emotional level. This enables you to operate at a higher level of visual literacy.

The next time you're listening to your favorite TED talk or attending a meeting, use the page opposite as a blank canvas and fill it with scribbles and shapes to keep your hands busy and your mind engaged. What you doodle next could be the key to a creative breakthrough.

DOODLING IS AN INCREDIBLY POWERFUL TOOL . . . THE DOODLE HAS NEVER BEEN THE NEMESIS OF INTELLECTUAL THOUGHT. IN REALITY, IT IS ONE OF ITS GREATEST ALLIES.

From "Doodler's Unite!" (2011)

Q For ideas about how to make the most of your doodles, see page 56 of *Great TED Talks: Creativity*

Get your doodle on:

DON'T LIKE THE WAY THINGS ARE DONE? SHAKE THEM UP!

Tom May,
*Great TED Talks:
Creativity*, page 24.

5. TURN OUT THE LIGHTS

Are you struggling to think of an idea? Turn out the lights and see what comes rushing in.

Take a moment tonight to consider some new ideas. Start off in a well-lit room and write down the ideas that come to mind. Now, turn out the lights and see what the darkness does to your creative thinking. When you have finished, turn on the lights and compare the two sets of thoughts. You should find that the ideas you wrote down in the light are more rational and scientific, whereas the dark presented more imaginative ideas. This is because the darkness influences our imaginations and allows us to think in a new way. Give this a try each time you need to think outside the box.

IN THE LIGHT ROOM PEOPLE TENDED TO CHOOSE MORE RATIONAL OR SCIENTIFIC EXPLANATIONS, BUT IN THE DARK ROOM PEOPLE WERE MORE INCLINED TO USE THEIR IMAGINARY THINKING.

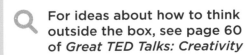

From "How Darkness Influences Imagination" (2016)

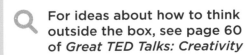

🔍 For ideas about how to think outside the box, see page 60 of *Great TED Talks: Creativity*

Think of an idea
First in the light and then in the dark . . .

Light:

Dark:

A NONEXPERT CAN OFTEN BE THE BEST PERSON TO HELP WITH A BREAKTHROUGH.

Tom May,
*Great TED Talks:
Creativity*, page 32.

6. DESIRE PATHS

Desire paths are the trails formed by people who stray from the footpaths and create their own route through a garden or park. Let desire paths for your product be created naturally and then pave over them.

These alternate trails are proof that what you create may not be exactly what people want but they can be used to your benefit. If you have an idea that you're struggling to reach the right solution for, why not examine the desire paths? Use the page opposite to detail your idea and the different routes available, then present this to your customers and see which options they prefer, detailing them underneath. This idea can be used in any creative endeavor, from chain restaurant menus to app design.

IT WAS AMAZING TO ME HOW MANY PEOPLE REFUSED TO TAKE THE LONG, MEANDERING PATH TO THE LEFT, AND JUST CUT THROUGH TO THE RIGHT.

From "What Can we Learn from Shortcuts?" (2016)

Q **For ideas about how to use feedback, see page 70 of** *Great TED Talks: Creativity*

Log your progress along your desire paths:

GET YOUR CREATIVE JUICES FLOWING BY ADDING TO AN IMAGINARY DICTIONARY.

Tom May,
Great TED Talks: Creativity, page 33.

FINDING WAYS TO WORK WITH THE WRONG EQUIPMENT CAN BE A BOOST TO YOUR CREATIVITY.

Tom May,
*Great TED Talks:
Creativity*, page 34.

7. YOUR IMPERFECT RÉSUMÉ

Selecting someone for a new role based on them having a good résumé might not give you the best person for the job. Open your mind to alternatives.

The quote below is a perfect example of where relying on old-fashioned job applications could result in you dismissing the best candidate without an interview. Think about yourself and fill the sheet opposite with your imperfect background. Now think about how you overcame those misfortunes. Being able to get through difficult times is a skill, so make sure you acknowledge it in others.

TAKE THIS RÉSUMÉ. THIS GUY'S PARENTS GIVE HIM UP FOR ADOPTION. HE NEVER FINISHES COLLEGE. HE JOB-HOPS QUITE A BIT, GOES ON A SOJOURN TO INDIA FOR A YEAR, AND TO TOP IT OFF, HE HAS DYSLEXIA. WOULD YOU HIRE THIS GUY? HIS NAME IS STEVE JOBS.

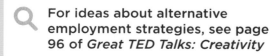

From "Why the Best Hire Might Not Have the Perfect Résumé" (2015)

Q For ideas about alternative employment strategies, see page 96 of *Great TED Talks: Creativity*

My imperfect résumé:

MULTITASKING ACTUALLY MAKES YOU *MORE* CREATIVE.

Tom May,
*Great TED Talks:
Creativity*, page 179.

WHATEVER YOUR DISCIPLINE, DRAWING CAN BE A USEFUL TOOL.

Tom May,
Great TED Talks: Creativity, page 158.

8. REJECTION BUCKET LIST

Rejection sucks but is it really that bad? This exercise might be just the thing to liberate you.

Every time you are faced with rejection, add it to your rejection bucket list opposite. Use this list as a way to remind yourself of when you've faced rejection and desensitize yourself. Each time you put yourself into a situation where you may be rejected you will feel a little calmer, until eventually most of your fear of rejection will disappear. This change in attitude will help you to put your ideas out there and it may just help them to take off.

REJECTION WAS MY CURSE, WAS MY BOOGEYMAN. IT HAS BOTHERED ME MY WHOLE LIFE BECAUSE I WAS RUNNING AWAY FROM IT. [WHEN] I STARTED EMBRACING IT, I TURNED THAT INTO THE BIGGEST GIFT IN MY LIFE.

From "What I Learned from 100 Days of Rejection" (2015)

Q For ideas about how to take rejection, see page 116 of *Great TED Talks: Creativity*

My rejection bucket list:

UNLOCK YOUR SUBCONSCIOUS WITH SIMPLE WORD PLAY.

Tom May,
*Great TED Talks:
Creativity*, page 52.

KILL YOUR PHONE AND SEE CREATIVITY COME RUSHING BACK.

Tom May,
*Great TED Talks:
Creativity*, page 54.

9. POSITIVE EXPERIENCE

Boost your happiness and boosts to your intelligence, creativity, and energy will follow.

Write down your positive experiences from the past 24 hours. Journaling about them allows your brain to relive it and absorb it. Happiness has been proven to increase our productivity by 31 percent compared to any other state. So give it a go and let your happiness inspire you.

Pass on your positivity by sending out one positive email a day to a member of your team.

JOURNALING ABOUT ONE POSITIVE EXPERIENCE YOU'VE HAD OVER THE PAST TWENTY-FOUR HOURS ALLOWS YOUR BRAIN TO RELIVE IT.

From "The Happy Secret to Better Work" (2011)

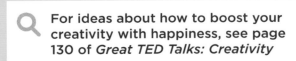

For ideas about how to boost your creativity with happiness, see page 130 of *Great TED Talks: Creativity*

My positive experiences:

DOODLE TO YOUR HEART'S CONTENT. IT COULD BE THE KEY TO A CREATIVE BREAKTHROUGH.

Tom May,
*Great TED Talks:
Creativity*, page 57.

10. WHAT IS FAILURE?

Are you afraid of failure? Here is a helpful tip to help you overcome your fears.

Use the page opposite to draw, write, or create failure. Try to answer the question "What if I fail?" with your creation. Now ask yourself "How will I recover?" and plot out exactly what you will do. Finally, ask yourself "What if I do nothing?" and note down your answer.

Confronting your worries head-on is the best way to tame them and turn them into fuel. Knowing exactly what scares you and having a plan for rehabilitating yourself will have a positive effect on lessening the initial fear. Failing may still be hard but it is no longer unmanageable. The final step then forces you to make the decision about whether your idea is worth facing failure for, or not.

WHAT IF I FAILED? WRITE IT OUT. PAINT A PICTURE. MAKE IT A MOVIE. MAKE IT AS VIVID AS YOU CAN.

From "Turning Fear Into Fuel" (2010)

Q For ideas about how to face failure, see page 141 of *Great TED Talks: Creativity*

What does failure look like? Draw it out and turn it into fuel.

STRUGGLING TO BEGIN? WRITE THE FIRST SENTENCE, THEN IMPROVISE.

Tom May,
Great TED Talks: Creativity, page 64.

11. THE "CAN'T-DO" LIST

Pushing the limits of what you can do will help you to discover that you can do more than you may think.

We all face challenges in our work but it's how we respond to them that counts—turn adversity to your advantage by using the page opposite to identify your "can't-do" list. Include things you may be struggling with from all aspects of your life. Once you have listed them, try to work out how you might be able to do them.

Facing new challenges head-on can evolve your creativity and help you to identify problems as an opportunity to find your true creative voice.

ARTISTS [OFTEN] SPEAK ABOUT HOW PUSHING THE LIMITS OF WHAT THEY CAN DO, SOMETIMES PUSHING INTO WHAT THEY CAN'T DO, HELPS THEM FOCUS ON FINDING THEIR OWN VOICE.

From "4 Lessons in Creativity" (2012)

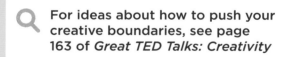

🔍 For ideas about how to push your creative boundaries, see page 163 of *Great TED Talks: Creativity*

My "can't-do" list:

☒ _____

☒ _____

☒ _____

☒ _____

☒ _____

☒ _____

☒ _____

☒ _____

☒ _____

☒ _____

☒ _____

☒ _____

☒ _____

☒ _____

☒ _____

DON'T OVERTHINK THINGS: LET YOUR INSTINCTS TAKE OVER.

Tom May,
*Great TED Talks:
Creativity*, page 65.

TRAVEL BROADENS THE MIND, BUT SO DOES GOING NOWHERE.

Tom May,
*Great TED Talks:
Creativity*, page 86.

12. ANCESTRAL BACKGROUND MAP

We can all benefit from learning from other cultures, but it can be even more beneficial to learn from your own personal background.

Harness your heritage by using the page opposite to draw your family tree. Is it linear or does it contain some mixed heritage? Do you know where your ancestors lived or where they worked? Dive as deep as possible into the people that make up your tree and use their stories to infuse your background into your creativity, whether it is art, literature, or music.

IT'S BEEN MY JOURNEY TO FIND MY VOICE, RECLAIM THE STORIES OF MY HERITAGE AND THE PAST, AND INFUSE THEM INTO MUSIC AND FILM.

From "Why Do I Make Art?
To Build Time Capsules for My Heritage" **(2017)**

For ways to shape your creative voice, see page 164 of *Great TED Talks: Creativity*

My family tree:

A FEW MINDFUL MINUTES IS ALL YOU NEED TO REBOOT YOUR BRAIN.

Tom May,
*Great TED Talks:
Creativity*, page 88.

13. MY MULTIPOTENTIALITY

Are you worried that you've not found your one true calling? It might be because some of us don't have just one.

Growing up you are told that you can only do one thing, so you don't embrace everything that you could be. This isn't true—some people are "multipotentialities." These people are able to bring a breadth of knowledge to the team.

Circle all the words that apply to you on the page opposite, then add some more. Embrace all your multipotentialities and use them to help you develop in the areas you are passionate about.

THE SPECIALISTS CAN DIVE IN DEEP AND IMPLEMENT IDEAS, WHILE THE MULTIPOTENTIALITE BRINGS A BREADTH OF KNOWLEDGE TO THE PROJECT. IT'S A BEAUTIFUL PARTNERSHIP.

From "Why Some of Us Don't Have One True Calling" (2015)

🔍 For ideas about how to embrace your multipotentiality, see page 178 of *Great TED Talks: Creativity*

I am:

Determined

A Friend

Resourceful

Dedicated

A Team player

An Advertiser

Visionary

Creative

Inspiring

A Leader

A Musician

An Artist

A Colleague

Intelligent

Strategic

A Writer

An Innovator

DON'T JUST WORK WITH A FEW PEOPLE; WORK WITH MILLIONS!

Tom May,
*Great TED Talks:
Creativity*, page 100.

THE OFFICE IS AN OUTDATED CONCEPT. IT'S TIME TO WORK ELSEWHERE.

Tom May,
Great TED Talks: Creativity, page 124.

14. DRAW YOUR PERSONAL FUTURE

Do you have a creative dream? Do you have trouble putting it into motion? This drawing exercise could help you make your vision a reality.

The key to achieving your dream future and your creative ideas is to visualize them. In order to do this it is important to be in the right frame of mind. First, you need to see it, then you can believe it and train your brain to execute it.

Use the boxes opposite to draw where you are now and where you want to be. You don't need to be an artist. When you've finished, think about how to connect the two images. This is your road map for change.

AS NAÏVE AS YOUR DRAWINGS MAY BE, WHEN YOU DRAW WHERE YOU ARE, YOUR CURRENT STATE, AND WHERE YOU WANT TO BE, YOUR DESIRED NEW REALITY, SUDDENLY YOU HAVE A ROAD MAP FOR CHANGE.

From "Draw Your Future—Take Control of Your Life" (2015)

Q **For ideas about how to create a road map for change, see page 185 of** *Great TED Talks: Creativity*

Where I am now:

Where I want to be:

EXERCISES

FOR

INNOVATION

15. KNOW YOUR BLIND SPOTS

Are you making bold choices with your eyes wide open? Do you know where your blind spots are?

The mind can blind us from reality and trick us into thinking we already know everything we need to in order to make a certain judgment or come up with a new idea. These unfounded assumptions prevent us from thinking creatively.

Use the boxes opposite to identify and overcome your blind spots. Now remove any cognitive bias by considering the ways in which you can overcome these biases. The aim of this task is to make you more self-aware, help you to learn from your imperfections, and enable a culture of innovation.

I USED TO THINK THE HUMAN BRAIN WAS THE MOST WONDERFUL ORGAN IN MY BODY. THEN I REALIZED WHO WAS TELLING ME THIS.

From "Where Are Your Blind Spots?" (2016)

Q For ideas about how to overcome your blind spots, see page 13 of *Great TED Talks: Innovation*

My blind spots:

SUCCESSFUL LEADERS IN A DIGITAL AGE UNDERSTAND THAT WE ARE DESIGNED TO CONNECT AND CONTRIBUTE.

Neil C. Hughes,
Great TED Talks: Innovation, page 32.

16. CHALLENGE YOURSELF

Find a voice outside your comfort zone by challenging yourself.

In the space opposite, write a challenge that you would like to overcome. This could be about being successful at work or being more creative at home. Once you've identified the area you would like to improve, look into the skills you would need to make this happen. How could you learn the skills you don't already have and improve the ones you already do? You now have a plan for how to succeed in obtaining your goal.

Remember that genuine innovators value innovation and help others on their journey, too. Try passing on what you have learned to your team.

THE FIRST THING YOU NEED IS A BIG CHALLENGE, SOMETHING THAT EXCITES YOU AND MAYBE SCARES YOU TOO. YOU THEN NEED THE SKILLS.

From "Can You Design an Innovative Culture?" (2016)

🔍 **For ideas on how to work outside of your comfort zone, see page 18 of *Great TED Talks: Innovation***

Challenge:

Necessary skills:

GOING FOR A WALK MIGHT BE ALL IT TAKES TO GET YOUR TEAM'S CREATIVE JUICES FLOWING.

Neil C. Hughes,
*Great TED Talks:
Innovation*, page 36.

17. DISRUPT OR BE DISRUPTED

Become a hyper-innovator by disrupting your product, design, and marketing.

The exercise opposite has been designed to make you think about how your product can be disrupted and how you can overcome these issues with hyper-innovation. First, come up with a product. Then, work out how you can disrupt it. This should lead you to consider new products or ways of designing and marketing your product so you can achieve hyper-innovation.

Start-ups embrace failure as a learning opportunity when racing ahead to secure a competitive advantage. Larger corporations need to be more cautious, so take advantage of your chance to embrace new ways of working.

ASK YOURSELF, WHAT DOES IT TAKE TO DISRUPT YOUR BUSINESS MODEL, TAKE YOUR VALUE CHAIN, AND CUT IT INTO PIECES AND PUT IT TOGETHER IN A DIFFERENT WAY.

From "Business Model Innovation: Beating Yourself at Your Own Game" (2014)

🔍 For ideas about how to become a hyper-innovator, see page 46 of *Great TED Talks: Innovation*

Can you beat yourself at your own game?

Disrupt your product

Disrupt your design

Disrupt your marketing

FIND OUT WHERE INNOVATIVE IDEAS COME FROM AND LEARN HOW YOU CAN REPLICATE THEM.

Neil C. Hughes,
*Great TED Talks:
Innovation*, page 42.

IF YOU WANT TO CHANGE THE WORLD, START WITH YOURSELF.

Neil C. Hughes,
*Great TED Talks:
Innovation*, page 142.

18. ASK FOR HELP

Asking for help can be daunting but there comes a time when it just can't be avoided, so invest some time in getting better at it.

The only way to become comfortable with it is to practice and improve. Try to avoid being awkward by being very specific about the help you want and why. Vague and indirect requests aren't very helpful. You're also much more likely to receive a positive response if you ask for help in person, rather than via email or text.

Completing the task opposite will help you to overcome your fear of asking for help and make you more innovative as a result. After all, we can't innovate alone.

IF WE'RE GOING TO ASK FOR HELP—AND WE HAVE TO, WE ALL DO, PRACTICALLY EVERY DAY—THE ONLY WAY WE'RE GOING TO GET COMFORTABLE WITH IT IS TO GET GOOD AT IT.

From "How to Ask for Help—And Get a 'Yes'" (2019)

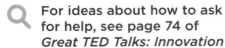

🔍 **For ideas about how to ask for help, see page 74 of** *Great TED Talks: Innovation*

Five ways you could ask for help:

INTROVERTS BRING EXTRAORDINARY TALENTS AND ABILITIES TO THE WORKPLACE AND SHOULD BE ENCOURAGED AND CELEBRATED.

Neil C. Hughes,
*Great TED Talks:
Innovation*, page 58.

19. A NEW CORPORATE DEMOCRACY

Rethink everything—from meetings to reporting vacation days—to create a new corporate democracy.

Many of the rules we have in place contradict our desire for innovation and a more collaborative environment. Think about the questions opposite: what do you do? Why do you do it? Have a go at writing down your responses. Does what you do prove what you believe? Identifying these key elements will help you to understand what people buy about you and how you can make yourself and your company more innovative.

PEOPLE DON'T BUY WHAT YOU DO; THEY BUY WHY YOU DO IT. AND WHAT YOU DO SIMPLY PROVES WHAT YOU BELIEVE.

From "How to Run a Company with (Almost) No Rules" (2015)

 For more ideas on corporate democracy, see page 84 of *Great TED Talks: Innovation*

What do you do?	Why do you do it?

WE NEED TO STOP LOOKING AT WASTE AS BEING USELESS AND LEARN HOW WE CAN TURN IT INTO ECO TREASURE.

Neil C. Hughes,
Great TED Talks:
Innovation, page 65.

LEARN TO IDENTIFY THE DESIRED PATH OF YOUR CUSTOMERS.

Neil C. Hughes,
Great TED Talks: Innovation, page 66.

20. THE NEW RULES OF INNOVATION

Innovation requires taking chances and challenging things we think we know with certainty, but it also rewards risk-taking and rule-breaking.

From looking at how the world is changing, it is clear that the old rules or ways of working are no longer relevant. Using your company as a starting point, list some rules opposite and check them off as you break them. Considering the rules and challenging them could be the key to unlocking your next big innovation.

THOSE WHO MAKE NEW INNOVATIONS AND ARE SUCCESSFUL IN BREAKING THE RULES ARE CREATING THE NEW RULES. AND IN A NEVER-ENDING CYCLE, THOSE NEW RULES WILL HAVE TO BE BROKEN AS WELL.

From "The New Rules of Innovation" (2012)

 For ideas about changing the rules, see page 91 of *Great TED Talks: Innovation*

Break some rules:

- [ ] _____
- [ ] _____
- [ ] _____
- [ ] _____
- [ ] _____
- [ ] _____
- [ ] _____
- [ ] _____
- [ ] _____
- [ ] _____
- [ ] _____
- [ ] _____
- [ ] _____
- [ ] _____
- [ ] _____

INCREASE YOUR LUCK BY VENTURING OUTSIDE OF THE SAFE ZONE.

Neil C. Hughes,
Great TED Talks: Creativity, page 106.

21. EXPLORE THE WEIRD AND UNKNOWN

Embrace strangers and strangeness to boost your creativity.

We are more connected than we have ever been, but having access to lots of content has also reinforced our fear of venturing out of the safety of what we have always known. Use the page opposite to consider everything and everyone you find strange. What is their world based around? How does this differ from your own worldview? Exploring these areas and meeting these people will lead to exciting discoveries and get you thinking more creatively.

IN THE CONTEXT OF THIS BROAD RANGE OF DIGITAL RELATIONS, SAFELY SEEKING STRANGENESS MIGHT VERY WELL BE A NEW BASIS FOR INNOVATION.

From "Why We Need Strangeness" (2013)

 For ideas about how to increase your creativity, see page 100 of *Great TED Talks: Innovation*

What do you find strange?

STOP WORRYING ABOUT THE FUTURE AND INNOVATE IN THE PRESENT.

Neil C. Hughes,
*Great TED Talks:
Innovation*, page 114.

22. FAILING MINDFULLY

Don't let failure define you. It is not just presenting you with an opportunity to learn but leaving you with a responsibility to fail mindfully.

Punishing failure stifles innovation and business creativity but simply celebrating it will not lead to innovation. The key to innovation in the face of failure is to fail mindfully. List three goals for the future on the page opposite and return to this task when you have completed them. Did you succeed or fail? If you failed, consider the impact and consequences of that failure, as well as the lessons learned. Sharing this information with your team could provide opportunities for others to innovate too.

YOU CAN MEASURE YOUR WORTH BY YOUR DEDICATION TO YOUR PATH, NOT BY YOUR SUCCESSES OR FAILURES.

From "Success, Failure, and the Drive to Keep Creating" (2014)

Q For more ideas about how to learn from failure, see page 118 of *Great TED Talks: Innovation*

My goals for the future:

1.

2.

3.

ONLY BY CONTINUOUSLY LEARNING AND IMPROVING CAN YOU GENUINELY UNDERSTAND THAT INNOVATION IS A JOURNEY, NOT A DESTINATION.

Neil C. Hughes,
*Great TED Talks:
Innovation*, page 120.

23. SPACE TO CREATE

Do you have a makerspace—a dedicated area for yourself or your team to share projects and ideas?

Having somewhere that encourages the collision of ideas and a designated area for collaboration can accelerate your innovation efforts and provide magical results. Use the page opposite to design your perfect makerspace. Where is it? What tools do you have there? Who would help you innovate? Remember, tools might be helpful but people are the key to innovation. Once you have your design, why not put it into action?

THERE'S A SAYING IN THE MAKER MOVEMENT. THEY CAME FOR THE TOOLS, BUT THEY STAYED FOR THE PEOPLE.

From "A Makerspace for Everyone" (2018)

For more about creative spaces, see page 163 of *Great TED Talks: Innovation*

My perfect makerspace:

_____

_____

_____

_____

_____

Tools

_____

_____

_____

_____

People

_____

_____

_____

_____

_____

WHAT WOULD YOU ATTEMPT TO DO IF YOU KNEW YOU COULD NOT FAIL?

Neil C. Hughes,
*Great TED Talks:
Innovation*, page 124.

24. CHANGING THE WORLD

What would you do if you could change the world? What causes are important to you? Would you focus your attention abroad or closer to home?

As an innovator, it's your responsibility to be the driving force of change. Use the page opposite to write your manifesto. Think about what you'd like to improve and what you're passionate about and include it. After all, passion is the driving force behind innovation, and innovation can change the world. Keep your manifesto to remind you about what is important to you and inspire you to innovate.

INNOVATION IS THE PROCESS OF CREATING SOMETHING NEW THAT MAKES LIFE BETTER. INNOVATION IS IMPOSSIBLE WITHOUT PASSION. INNOVATORS SEE THE WORLD DIFFERENTLY.

From "Innovating to Zero" (2010)

For more about how innovation can change the world, see page 174 of *Great TED Talks: Innovation*

My manifesto:

ALWAYS LOOK FOR WAYS TO TRANSFORM ADVERSITY INTO OPPORTUNITY.

Neil C. Hughes,
*Great TED Talks:
Innovation*, page 126.

25. TAKE CONTROL OF YOUR DESTINY

Overcome self-doubt and secure your own successes by reconsidering what is important to you.

Use the page opposite to write your ultimate bucket list and check off the items as you complete them. Include everything you want to do but make sure you're passionate about them. By avoiding doing things you hate and refocusing your efforts on patience and passion, you will be providing yourself with the tools to overcome self-doubt and put yourself in a position to enable success.

YOUR LEGACY IS BEING WRITTEN BY YOURSELF. SO, MAKE THE RIGHT DECISIONS.

From "Do What You Love (No Excuses!)" (2008)

For more ideas about how to take control, see page 180 of *Great TED Talks: Innovation*

My ultimate bucket list:

❑

❑

❑

❑

❑

❑

❑

❑

❑

❑

❑

❑

❑

❑

❑

EXERCISES

FOR

LEADERSHIP

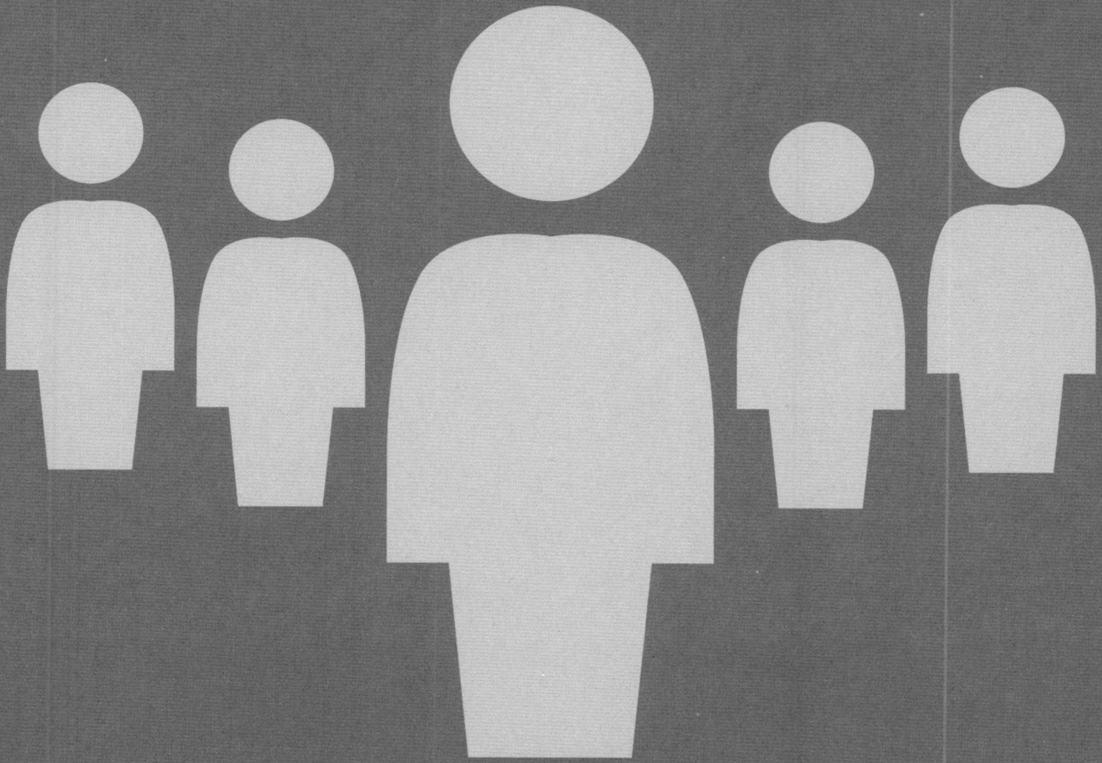

26. STRESS IS YOUR FRIEND

It has long been believed that stress is harmful to your health and is the enemy of creativity and innovation . . . but it doesn't have to be. Learn to use it to your advantage.

The body's stress responses can have a positive effect and understanding this fact should help your body to behave in a much healthier way. Use the exercise opposite to list three sources that cause you stress. Now, try to think of stress as a positive driving force and something that is helpful for our performance. Just looking at stress in this new way should help you to manage your physical health as you progress in your career and encounter increasingly stressful situations.

WHEN YOU CHOOSE TO VIEW YOUR STRESS RESPONSE AS HELPFUL, YOU CREATE THE BIOLOGY OF COURAGE. AND WHEN YOU CHOOSE TO CONNECT WITH OTHERS UNDER STRESS, YOU CAN CREATE RESILIENCE.

From "How to Make Stress Your Friend" (2013)

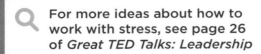

> Q For more ideas about how to work with stress, see page 26 of *Great TED Talks: Leadership*

My stress list:

Stress 1

Stress 2

Stress 3

PRACTICE, FAIL, PRACTICE MORE, AND TRY AGAIN.

Harriet Minter,
Great TED Talks: Leadership, page 11.

WHEN WE FOCUS ONLY ON THE GOAL, WE MISS OUT ON THE BEAUTY OF WHERE WE ARE NOW.

Harriet Minter,
*Great TED Talks:
Leadership*, page 14.

27. KEEP IT SIMPLE

Don't let creating a strategy overwhelm you. Break it down and organize it.

Using the headings opposite, create a strategy to manage your team. Ask yourself what you need in terms of resources, support, and structure. Next, organize yourself and your resources. Then, break your vision into short-term goals and match each piece of your strategy with these smaller targets. Now that you have a fully organized strategy, you can start to execute it. Stay organized and managing others won't seem too difficult.

INNOVATE, STRATEGIZE, ORGANIZE, AND ENERGIZE. IF YOU CAN DO THOSE FOUR THINGS, I BELIEVE THAT WHATEVER STAGE OF MANAGEMENT YOU'RE IN, YOU'RE GOING TO BE SUCCESSFUL.

From "Strategic Planning in Practice" (2017)

Q **For more ideas about creating a strategy, see page 76 of** *Great TED Talks: Leadership*

Plan your idea . . .

Innovate

Strategize

Organize

Energize

WE ALL HAVE A RIGHT TO BE SEEN AND HEARD. SHARING OUR PROBLEMS WITH THOSE AROUND US CAN HELP US GET THROUGH THEM.

Harriet Minter,
*Great TED Talks:
Leadership*, page 18.

A KEY COMPONENT OF RESILIENCE IS COMMUNITY. FIND THOSE FIGHTING THE SAME FIGHT AS YOU ARE AND ALLOW THEM TO LIFT YOU UP.

Harriet Minter,
*Great TED Talks:
Leadership*, page 22.

WITHOUT PUSHING THROUGH DIFFICULT TIMES, WE SIMPLY WON'T GROW.

Harriet Minter,
*Great TED Talks:
Leadership*, page 23.

28. FIND A MENTOR

Finding someone who can help fill the gaps in your knowledge will help you to achieve the things you set out to do.

Your mentors can be people, but if you're struggling to tap into the knowledge you need, a good alternative is a book. Use the page opposite to list the people and authors that inspire you. If you don't already know them, go out and discover them. When you're looking for a mentor, seek answers from a range of people and find a mentor who can help you build your strategy through their own life experience. When you have completed your list start reading or speaking to your mentors to improve your leadership skills.

THERE'S A MYTH THAT YOU HAVE TO GO INWARD TO FIND THE TRUTH. BUT THE TRUTH . . . IS THAT YOU HAVE TO GO OUTWARD.

From "Why I Read a Book a Day (and Why You Should Too): The Law of the 33%" (2015)

 For tips on finding a mentor, see page 78 of *Great TED Talks: Leadership*

My mentor list:

1. _____

2. _____

3. _____

4. _____

5. _____

6. _____

7. _____

8. _____

9. _____

10. _____

TALK LESS AND LISTEN MORE.

Harriet Minter,
*Great TED Talks:
Leadership*, page 44.

HAVE YOU EVER BEEN SO IN LOVE WITH AN IDEA THAT YOU'VE COMPLETELY FAILED TO SEE THE FLAWS IN IT?

Harriet Minter,
*Great TED Talks:
Leadership*, page 36.

29. DON'T FORGET TO FORGET

Give yourself the opportunity to let go of things as well as to remember them by setting yourself targets.

Use the page opposite to make a 200-year plan. Set milestones for the things you want to achieve and the things you want to let go of. Use this as a strategy for keeping what serves you and letting go of the rest. Acknowledge the parts of your history that you are hanging on to and ask yourself whether they are still serving you. If they are not, use the exercise to work out when they will become irrelevant and give yourself a date for letting go. Doing this enough will help you to redefine yourself.

YOU KNOW, WE CARRY SO MUCH BAGGAGE, FROM OUR PARENTS, FROM OUR SOCIETY, FROM SO MANY PEOPLE—FEARS, INSECURITIES—AND OUR 200-YEAR PLAN REALLY LISTS ALL OUR CHILDHOOD PROBLEMS THAT WE HAVE TO EXPIRE.

From "What's Your 200-Year Plan?" (2012)

 For ideas about letting go, see page 80 of *Great TED Talks: Leadership*

My 200-year plan:

SOMETIMES PEOPLE CAN'T TELL US THEY NEED HELP; WE HAVE TO LOOK FOR THE SIGNS.

Harriet Minter,
*Great TED Talks:
Leadership*, page 45.

YOU CAN HAVE THE GREATEST VISION IN THE WORLD, BUT IF YOU CAN'T BRING PEOPLE WITH YOU, IT WILL NEVER BE ANYTHING MORE THAN AN IDEA.

Harriet Minter,
Great TED Talks: Leadership, page 53.

30. STAND OUT

Stop mimicking the successes of those around you and start to create your own vision.

On the page opposite, celebrate three things that make you stand out. We often hide the parts of ourselves we feel insecure about, but what makes us stand out from the crowd is often our most important asset. Taking the time to consider your differences and working out how to use them to your advantage will help you to succeed as a leader and encourage others to do the same.

I WANT TO ENCOURAGE YOUNG PEOPLE TO ASPIRE TO DREAM. I WANT PEOPLE TO UNDERSTAND THAT IT'S OKAY TO BE DIFFERENT; IT'S OKAY TO STAND OUT. I'M DIFFERENT.

From "From 'Devil's Child' to Star Ballerina" (2014)

Q For more ideas about standing out, see page 82 of *Great TED Talks: Leadership*

What makes me different?

DON'T WAIT TO BE TOLD IT'S POSSIBLE—DREAM BIG. THEN MAKE THE DREAM POSSIBLE.

Harriet Minter,
*Great TED Talks:
Leadership*, page 60.

YOU DON'T HAVE TO HAVE ALL THE ANSWERS. FINDING SOMEONE WHO HAS ALREADY ACHIEVED WHAT YOU WANT WILL HELP YOU START TO SEE WHAT NEEDS TO BE DONE.

Harriet Minter,
*Great TED Talks:
Leadership*, page 78.

31. YOU'RE ALREADY A LEADER

Leadership doesn't have to be something we think about ourselves—you may find that other people see you as a leader without you realizing.

Look at yourself subjectively and list the qualities that other people might consider make you a leader on the opposite page. When you've finished, ask others for their experiences of you and the impact you've had on their life. Compare what you listed to the responses you received. Are there any characteristics that appear in both lists? Use what you have learned to help you understand all of the qualities that make someone a leader.

WE'VE MADE LEADERSHIP ABOUT CHANGING THE WORLD, AND THERE IS NO WORLD. THERE'S ONLY SIX BILLION UNDERSTANDINGS OF IT.

From "Everyday Leadership" (2010)

🔍 **For ideas about how to be a better leader, see page 142 of** *Great TED Talks: Leadership*

What makes you a leader?

BY DEVELOPING A GROWTH MIND-SET, WE CAN ADAPT AND LEARN RATHER THAN EXPECTING TO HAVE ALL THE ANSWERS RIGHT NOW.

Harriet Minter,
*Great TED Talks:
Leadership*, page 94.

JUST AS FEAR CAN BE CONTAGIOUS, SO CAN COURAGE. WHEN WE TAKE BOLD ACTIONS, WE PASS THAT BRAVERY ON TO OTHERS.

Harriet Minter,
*Great TED Talks:
Leadership*, page 97.

32. GET PRAISE

Part of being a leader is accepting that if we're not getting what we need to lead well, then we need to ask for it.

Do you feel like you've done a good job but haven't been recognized? Write a letter of appreciation to yourself. Getting positive feedback not only enhances your mental well-being, but it can also enhance your performance, even if it is from yourself. Eventually you should feel confident enough to ask for the praise you deserve, which will make you a better leader and help your team to thrive.

MAYBE SOMEBODY'S NEVER SAID THAT TO YOU, BUT YOU'VE DONE A REALLY, REALLY GOOD JOB. AND THANK YOU FOR BEING HERE, JUST SHOWING UP AND CHANGING THE WORLD WITH YOUR IDEAS.

From "Remember to Say Thank You" (2008)

For more information on asking for praise, see page 172 of *Great TED Talks: Leadership*

Letter of appreciation to myself:

WHEN IT FEELS LIKE EVERYONE IS FIGHTING US, WE CAN EITHER FIGHT BACK OR WE CAN TAKE A DIFFERENT APPROACH.

Harriet Minter,
*Great TED Talks:
Leadership*, page 167.

BE BRAVE ENOUGH TO TELL PEOPLE THE THINGS THEY DON'T WANT TO HEAR.

Harriet Minter,
*Great TED Talks:
Leadership*, page 102.

33. MINDFUL CURIOSITY

When we get used to working in one particular way, shifting into another pattern can be difficult. Become a better leader by breaking out of your habits and becoming more agile.

Use the page opposite to identify and overcome your habits. If you've had a piece of feedback that requires you to change your behavior and yet you find yourself reluctant to do so, spend some time being curious about how you feel when you're leading in that style. What are the benefits and what are the negatives? What would be possible if you could flex your style? The more we practice this mindfulness, the more we're able to become aware of our patterns and shift them accordingly to enable a culture of innovation.

JUST BE CURIOUSLY AWARE OF WHAT'S HAPPENING IN YOUR BODY AND MIND IN THAT MOMENT. IT WILL JUST BE ANOTHER CHANCE TO PERPETUATE ONE OF OUR ENDLESS AND EXHAUSTIVE HABIT LOOPS . . . OR STEP OUT OF IT.

From "A Simple Way to Break a Bad Habit" (2015)

🔍 For more inspiration about mindful curiosity, see page 183 of *Great TED Talks: Leadership*

My habits:

WHEN YOU FIND YOURSELF ANXIOUS ABOUT A BIG EVENT, FOCUS YOUR ATTENTION ON THE MOMENTS BEFORE IT RATHER THAN ON THE EVENT ITSELF.

Harriet Minter,
*Great TED Talks:
Leadership*, page 106.

YOUR UNIQUE EXPERIENCES WILL ALLOW YOU TO BUILD BRIDGES BETWEEN DIFFERENT WORLDS.

Harriet Minter,
Great TED Talks: Leadership, page 112.

34. RESPECT IS KEY

How do you persuade someone who disagrees with you of the value
of your argument?

When two opposing sides argue their point of view, they do so based on the moral
values they believe to be most important. This results in each participant trying
to convince the other of their own opinion. Therefore, it is helpful to connect any
argument to the underlying moral values of the person you are speaking to. Use
the page opposite to rehearse how you might persuade a member of your team
about a new policy you'd like to introduce. Remember to think beyond your own
reasons, taking the time to understand where they're coming from and respect it.

IF YOU WANT TO PERSUADE SOMEONE ON SOME POLICY, IT'S HELPFUL TO CONNECT THAT POLICY TO THEIR UNDERLYING MORAL VALUES. AND WHEN YOU SAY IT LIKE THAT, IT SEEMS REALLY OBVIOUS.

From "How to Have Better Political Conversations" (2016)

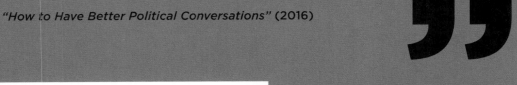

🔍 For more ideas about how to
persuade your team, see page
42 of *Great TED Talks: Leadership*

Why I believe: | **Why they would believe:**

LOOK TO COLLABORATE WITH PEOPLE WHO, IN THE PURSUIT OF THEIR OWN GOAL, WILL HELP YOU WITH YOURS.

Harriet Minter,
*Great TED Talks:
Leadership*, page 119.

35. KNOW YOUR IMPACT

It's easy to see only the detail of what you do day-to-day in your role and fail to see the bigger picture. Make sure you take the time to consider why your actions are important.

Think of three small actions you have completed as part of your day-to-day tasks. Now, write down the differences those actions made on the page opposite. This task should remind you that your job is about more than the everyday issues and help you to identify the impact of your actions and how this contributes to your company's overall vision. Consider how you brief your team members to make sure you are communicating the importance of achieving your overall vision.

IT'S NOT ABOUT SELLING SOAP, IT'S ABOUT MAKING SURE THAT IN THE PROCESS OF DOING SO YOU CAN CHANGE PEOPLE'S LIVES. SMALL ACTIONS, BIG DIFFERENCE."

From "Profit's Not Always the Point" (2013)

Q **For more about knowing your impact, see page 62 of *Great TED Talks: Leadership***

My actions and reactions:

1.

2.

3.

IF YOU WANT TO LEAD A TRULY COLLABORATIVE TEAM, THE FIRST THING YOU NEED TO DO IS PUT DOWN YOUR OWN EGO.

Harriet Minter,
*Great TED Talks:
Leadership*, page 120.

IT'S TIME TO REFRAME FAILURE AS SOMETHING THAT'S INEVITABLE IN OUR DRIVE FOR PERFECTION.

Harriet Minter,
*Great TED Talks:
Leadership*, page 166.

36. YOU CAN'T KNOW EVERYTHING

It's impossible to know everything, which is why asking people their opinions and advice is so valuable.

As a leader you may be able to see that there is a problem but lack the data and resources to solve it. Ask five different people what they think about your latest idea and note down their responses on the page opposite. Do you agree with their comments? Can you use them to improve your idea so that it will receive more positive feedback next time? Acknowledging your shortcomings and seeking help to fill gaps in your knowledge will improve your leadership skills.

ASK FIVE DIFFERENT PEOPLE WHAT'S GOING ON IN ORBIT. . . AND YOU'RE PROBABLY GOING TO GET TEN DIFFERENT ANSWERS.

From "The World's First Crowdsourced Space Traffic Monitoring System" (2019)

🔍 **For more information on crowdsourcing, see page 20 of *Great TED Talks: Leadership***

Five opinions:

1.

2.

3.

4.

5.

IF YOU WANT TO FIND AN INNOVATIVE SOLUTION TO A PROBLEM, START BY LIMITING THE RESOURCES YOU HAVE TO SOLVE IT.

Harriet Minter,
*Great TED Talks:
Leadership*, page 180.

WHAT WORKED WELL THIS WEEK? WHAT DIDN'T WORK WELL? AND WHAT WILL WE AGREE TO WORK ON IN THE WEEK AHEAD?

Harriet Minter,
*Great TED Talks:
Leadership*, page 184.